ACHIEVE LEVEL 6

MATHEMATICS
Practice
Questions

Hilary Koll
and Steve Mills

RISING ★ STARS

Rising Stars UK Ltd, 7 Hatchers Mews, Bermondsey Street,
London SE1 3GS
www.risingstars-uk.com

All facts are correct at time of going to press.

Published 2013
Reprinted with revisions 2013
Text, design and layout © 2013 Rising Stars UK Ltd

Project manager: Dawn Booth
Editorial: David Hemsley
Proofreader: Bobby Francis
Design: Words & Pictures Ltd, London
Cover design: Marc Burville-Riley

British Library Cataloguing-in-Publication Data
A CIP record for this book is available from the British Library.

ISBN: 978-0-85769-664-9
Printed in India by Multivista Global Ltd

Contents

How to use this book   4
Key facts   6
Test techniques   8

Section 1:
Level 5 – The tricky bits   9

Calculating percentages of amounts   9
Negative numbers   10
Long division   11
Multiplying and dividing decimals   12
Formulae   13
Ratio and proportion   14
Areas and perimeters of rectangles   15

Section 2:
Number and algebra   16

Adding and subtracting fractions and
  mixed numbers   16
Fraction, decimal and percentage equivalents   18
Percentage change   19
Writing a number as a fraction or percentage
  of another   20
Using ratios to divide amounts   22
Proportional reasoning   23
Adding and subtracting negative numbers   24
Using formulae   25
Trial and improvement   26
Solving simple linear equations   28
Expanding brackets   30
Finding a rule for the nth term of a sequence   31
Drawing straight line graphs   32
Describing straight line graphs   34

Section 3:
Shape, space and measures   36

Plans and elevations   36
Nets and 2-D representations of 3-D shapes   37
Quadrilaterals   38
Angles of polygons   40
Angles between lines   42
Areas of shapes made from rectangles   44
The circumference of a circle   45
The area of a circle   46
The volume of a cuboid   47
Transformations   48
Enlarging shapes   49

Section 4:
Handling data   50

Frequency diagrams   50
Scatter graphs   52
Pie charts   54
Probability – outcomes   55
Mutually exclusive events   56

Section 5:
Using and applying mathematics   57

Answers   Centre pull-out

How to use this book

Level 5 Tricky Bits practice questions

1 A set of warm-up practice questions, organised by topic. Provides practice in all the Level 5 Tricky Bits included in the Achieve Level 6 Maths Revision book.

2 Each question has space for the answers and a specific number of marks (like a real National Test question). Answers are included in the middle of the book.

3 Marking guidance is provided.

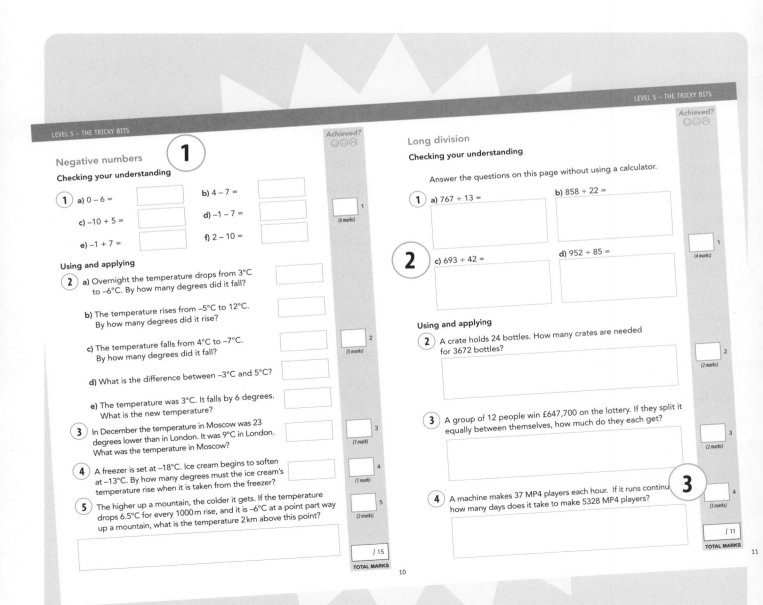

Topic questions

(1) Sets of questions on all the topics you need to cover for the Maths National Tests. Each topic includes some questions on using and applying mathematics.

(2) Each topic matches a section in the Achieve Level 6 Maths Revision book.

(3) Each question has space for the answers and a specific number of marks (like a real National Test question). Answers are included in the middle of the book.

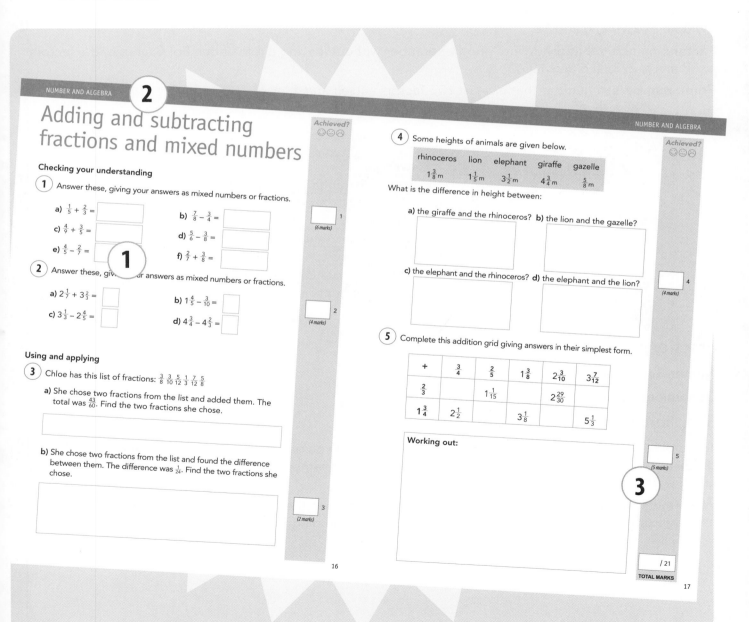

Key facts

Place value

The position of a digit in a number gives its value.

Ten thousands		Thousands		Hundreds		Tens		Units		Tenths		Hundredths	
40,000	+	7000	+	300	+	20	+	7	+	0.6	+	0.04	= 47,327.64

Rounding

Remember that 5 is rounded upwards, so 48.25 rounds up to 48.3.

Positive and negative integers

Integers are just whole numbers.

Remember to count 0 when counting from negative to positive and vice versa.

Properties of number

Square: the number made when a number is multiplied by itself.

Multiple: numbers in a number's times table. For example, some multiples of 3 are 3, 6, 36, 72 and 147.

Common multiples: multiples that are the same for different numbers. For example, 12 is a common multiple of 2, 3, 4, 6 and 12.

Factors: numbers that divide into another number without leaving a remainder. For example, the factors of 12 are 1, 2, 3, 4, 6 and 12.

Prime numbers: a number that has just two factors – itself and 1.

Tests of divisibility

A number can be divided by	If
2	it is even.
3	the sum of its digits is divisible by 3.
4	its last two digits are divisible by 4.
5	it ends in 5 or 0.
6	it is divisible by 2 and 3.
7	no 'ifs'. You have to work this one out the hard way!
8	half of the number can be divided by 4.
9	the sum of its digits is divisible by 9.
10	it ends in 0.

Fractions

Numerators tell us how many equal parts we have.

Denominators tell us how many equal parts there are.

Simplifying fractions

To simplify a fraction to its simplest form (or lowest terms) you need to find a common factor you can divide into both the numerator and the denominator. For example, to simplify $\frac{12}{16}$ divide the numerator and the denominator by 4: $\frac{12}{16} = \frac{3}{4}$

When multiplying fractions, multiply the numerators together, then multiply the denominators together and then simplify. For example, $\frac{3}{5} \times \frac{5}{6} = \frac{15}{30} = \frac{1}{2}$ (You can diagonally cancel first if it is easier.)

Fraction, decimal and percentage equivalents

Remember these equivalents:

Fraction	$\frac{1}{2}$	$\frac{1}{4}$	$\frac{1}{10}$	$\frac{3}{4}$	$\frac{1}{3}$
Decimal	0.5	0.25	0.1	0.75	0.33 (approximately)
Percentage	50%	25%	10%	75%	33% (approximately)

Ratio and proportion

Ratio is 'to every'. **Proportion** is 'for every' and can be given as a fraction, decimal or percentage.

You should simplify ratios and proportions to their simplest form.

Checking answers

Inverse means opposite. Check addition by subtraction and vice versa. Check multiplication by division and vice versa.

Addition and subtraction of decimals

Line up the decimal points when you write out the calculation.

Fill any empty spaces with a 0. Remember to put the decimal point in the answer.

Brackets

Always do the brackets in equations first.

Sometimes the mnemonic **BODMAS** is used to remind you that you do **b**rackets first, then **o**ther things like squaring or powers, then **d**ivision and **m**ultiplication and finally **a**ddition and **s**ubtraction.

2-D shapes

Perpendicular lines make a right angle. Parallel lines never meet. They can be straight or curved.

Triangles

Equilateral triangles have three equal sides and three equal angles. **Isosceles triangles** have two equal sides and two equal angles. **Scalene triangles** have three sides of different length and three angles of different sizes. **Right-angled triangles** can be isosceles or scalene.

Transforming 2-D shapes

When you draw reflections, remember to keep the correct distance from the mirror line. Rotational symmetry is about how many ways a shape can fit exactly on top of itself. When translating a shape, move it across first and then up or down.

Coordinates

Always read along the x-axis and then up or down the y-axis.

Always write x before y, i.e. (x and y).

Approximate metric and imperial conversions

1 litre = 1.8 pints	1 kilogram = 2.2 lbs (pounds)	1 pound = 0.454 kg
1 mile = 1.6 m	5 miles = 8 km	1 foot = 30 cm
1 metre = 3 feet 3 inches	1 inch = 2.5 cm	Milli = $\frac{1}{1000}$
Centi = $\frac{1}{100}$	Cent = 100	Kilo = 1000

Area of a rectangle

Area of a rectangle = length (*l*) × width (*w*).

Averages

Mean is the sum of all values divided by the number of values.
Median is the middle value when a list of values has been written in order.
Mode is the most common value.
Range is the difference between the highest and lowest value.

Test techniques

Before the test

1. When you revise, try revising a 'little and often' rather than in long sessions.
2. Learn your multiplication facts up to 10 × 10 so that you can recall them instantly. These are your tools for performing your calculations.
3. Revise with a friend. You can encourage and learn from each other.
4. Get a good night's sleep the night before.
5. Be prepared – bring your own pens and pencils.

During the test

1. Don't rush the first few questions. These tend to be quite straightforward, so don't make any silly mistakes.
2. As you know by now, READ THE QUESTION THEN READ IT AGAIN.
3. If you get stuck, don't linger on the same question – move on! You can come back to it later!
4. Never leave a multiple choice question. Make an educated guess if you really can't work out the answer.
5. Check how many marks a question is worth. Have you 'earned' those marks with your answer?
6. Check your answers. You can use the inverse method or rounding method. Does your answer look correct?
7. Be aware of the time. After 20 minutes, check to see how far you have got.
8. Leave a couple of minutes at the end to read through what you have written.
9. Always show your method. You may get a mark for showing you have gone through the correct procedure even if your answer is wrong.
10. Don't leave any questions unanswered. In the two minutes you have left yourself at the end, make an educated guess at the questions you really couldn't do.

Things to remember

1. If you see a difficult question, take your time, re-read it and have a go!
2. Check every question and every page to be sure you don't miss any!
3. If a question is about measuring, always write in the UNIT OF MEASUREMENT.
4. Don't be afraid to ask a teacher for anything you need, such as tracing paper or a protractor.
5. Write neatly – if you want to change an answer, put a line through it and write beside the answer box.
6. Always double-check your answers.

Level 5 – The tricky bits

Calculating percentages of amounts

Checking your understanding

1 Answer these questions without a calculator.

a) 5% of 3600 =

b) 15% of 320 =

c) 70% of 7000 =

d) 41% of 600 =

(4 marks) 1

2 Answer these questions using a calculator.

a) 47% of 45,800 =

b) 96% of 6800 =

c) 54% of 16,500 =

d) 78% of 42,000 =

(4 marks) 2

Using and applying

3 Answer these questions without a calculator.

a) 61% of 3400 people at a concert were men. How many were women?

(2 marks) 3

b) A business had an income of £88,000 in a year. 15% of that was spent on wages and expenses. The rest is profit. How much is profit?

You can use a calculator to answer questions 4 and 5.

4 James was given a bonus of 27% of his salary. His salary is £19,500. How much was his bonus?

(1 mark) 4

5 48% of the price of a book goes to the bookshop, 37% goes to the publisher and the rest goes to the author. For each book that costs £3.20, how much does the author get?

(2 marks) 5

/ 13

TOTAL MARKS

Achieved?

Negative numbers

Checking your understanding

1 **a)** 0 – 6 = [   ]   **b)** 4 – 7 = [   ]

c) –10 + 5 = [   ]   **d)** –1 – 7 = [   ]

e) –1 + 7 = [   ]   **f)** 2 – 10 = [   ]

[   ] 1
(6 marks)

Using and applying

2 **a)** Overnight the temperature drops from 3°C to –6°C. By how many degrees did it fall? [   ]

b) The temperature rises from –5°C to 12°C. By how many degrees did it rise? [   ]

c) The temperature falls from 4°C to –7°C. By how many degrees did it fall? [   ]

[   ] 2
(5 marks)

d) What is the difference between –3°C and 5°C? [   ]

e) The temperature was 3°C. It falls by 6 degrees. What is the new temperature? [   ]

3 In December the temperature in Moscow was 23 degrees lower than in London. It was 9°C in London. What was the temperature in Moscow? [   ]

[   ] 3
(1 mark)

4 A freezer is set at –18°C. Ice cream begins to soften at –13°C. By how many degrees must the ice cream's temperature rise when it is taken from the freezer? [   ]

[   ] 4
(1 mark)

5 The higher up a mountain, the colder it gets. If the temperature drops 6.5°C for every 1000 m rise, and it is –6°C at a point part way up a mountain, what is the temperature 2 km above this point?

[   ] 5
(2 marks)

[   ]

[   ] / 15

TOTAL MARKS

Long division

Achieved?
☺ ☺ ☹

Checking your understanding

Answer the questions on this page without using a calculator.

1 **a)** 767 ÷ 13 =

b) 858 ÷ 22 =

c) 693 ÷ 42 =

d) 952 ÷ 85 =

| 1 |
(4 marks)

Using and applying

2 A crate holds 24 bottles. How many crates are needed for 3672 bottles?

| 2 |
(2 marks)

3 A group of 12 people win £647,700 on the lottery. If they split it equally between themselves, how much do they each get?

| 3 |
(2 marks)

4 A machine makes 37 MP4 players each hour. If it runs continuously, how many days does it take to make 5328 MP4 players?

| 4 |
(3 marks)

| / 11 |

TOTAL MARKS

Multiplying and dividing decimals

Answer the questions on this page without using a calculator.

Checking your understanding

1 **a)** 5.2 × 3.4 =

b) 0.72 × 6.9 =

c) 1.67 × 5.8 =

d) 53.8 × 2.6 =

(4 marks) 1

2

a) 56.6 ÷ 4 =

b) 53.3 ÷ 2.6 =

c) 18.85 ÷ 14.5 =

d) 9.734 ÷ 6.2 =

(4 marks) 2

Using and applying

3 Clive equally shared £69.40 between his four daughters. How much did each daughter get?

(2 marks) 3

4 A rectangle has a length of 5.7 cm and a width of 3.9 cm. How large is its area?

(2 marks) 4

5 What is the average speed of a car that travels 135.24 km in 2.3 hours?

(2 marks) 5

Achieved?

/ 14

TOTAL MARKS

12

Formulae

Checking your understanding

1 Write a formula that shows the answer (A) you get when you:

a) divide a number (N) by 2 and subtract 5.

b) multiply a number (N) by 3 and add 7.

c) subtract 2 from a number (N) and multiply by 6.

d) add 4 to a number (N) and divide by 3.

| | 1 |
(4 marks)

Using and applying

2 **a)** At a funfair there is a £3 entrance fee and then each ride costs £4. Write a formula to show the total cost (T) in pounds for entering the funfair and then going on N rides.

b) What is the total cost (T) of entering the funfair and going on 8 rides?

| | 2 |
(2 marks)

3 **a)** The average speed (S) that Dan cycles at can be worked out by dividing the distance (D) he cycles by the time (T) he cycles. Write a formula for this.

b) If Dan cycles a distance of 117km in 3 hours, what was his average speed?

| | 3 |
(2 marks)

4 **a)** The distance (D) that Dan cycles at can be worked out by multiplying the speed (S) he cycles by the time (T) he cycles. Write a formula for this.

b) If Dan cycles for 4 hours at a speed of 32 km/hour what distance did he cycle?

| | 4 |
(2 marks)

| / 10 |

TOTAL MARKS

Ratio and proportion

Checking your understanding

1 Simplify each ratio.

a) 3:9 [ ]   **b)** 4:10 [ ]   **c)** 12:28 [ ]

d) 40:70 [ ]   **e)** 15:35 [ ]   **f)** 36:42 [ ]

1 [ ] *(6 marks)*

2 Look at this coloured rod.

Write, in its simplest form:

a) the ratio of blue to white sections. [ ]

b) the proportion of the rod that is blue. [ ]

2 [ ] *(2 marks)*

Using and applying

3 **a)** At a party there were 27 girls and 30 boys. What was the ratio of girls to boys? Give your answer in its simplest form. [ ]

b) In Class A there are 3 girls for every 4 boys. If there are 12 girls, how many are boys? Give your answer in its simplest form. [ ]

3 [ ] *(4 marks)*

4 Jeff gives some money to three workers. He gives £45 to Alan, £35 to Ben and £25 to Callum. Write this as a ratio in its simplest form. [ ]

4 [ ] *(1 mark)*

5 One-quarter of a box of chocolates are milk chocolate, one-third are dark chocolate and the rest are white chocolate. If there are 24 chocolates in the box, how many of the chocolates are:

a) milk? [ ]   **b)** dark? [ ]   **c)** white? [ ]

5 [ ] *(4 marks)*

d) What is the ratio of milk to dark to white chocolates in its simplest form?

[ ]

Achieved? ☺ ☹ ☹

/ 17

TOTAL MARKS

Areas and perimeters of rectangles

Checking your understanding

1 Find the perimeter and area of each rectangle

a)

4 cm

9 cm

Perimeter =

Area =

b)

3 cm

11 cm

Perimeter =

Area =

c)

5.5 cm

9 cm

Perimeter =

Area =

d)

2.5 cm

3 cm

Perimeter =

Area =

Using and applying

2 A rectangle has a perimeter of 16 cm and an area of 15 cm². What is its length and width?

3 Hannah wants to put wallpaper on one wall of her bedroom. The wall measures 2.5 m by 6 m. If the wallpaper she wants costs £1.20 per m², what is the minimum amount she would have to pay for it?

4 A rug is 64 cm wide. It has an area of 1.6 m². What is its length?

Achieved?

☺ ☺ ☹

1

(8 marks)

2

(2 marks)

3

(2 marks)

4

(1 mark)

/ 13

TOTAL MARKS

15

Adding and subtracting fractions and mixed numbers

Checking your understanding

1 Answer these, giving your answers as mixed numbers or fractions.

a) $\frac{1}{5} + \frac{2}{3} =$ ⬚

b) $\frac{7}{8} - \frac{3}{4} =$ ⬚

c) $\frac{4}{9} + \frac{3}{5} =$ ⬚

d) $\frac{5}{6} - \frac{3}{8} =$ ⬚

e) $\frac{4}{5} - \frac{2}{7} =$ ⬚

f) $\frac{2}{7} + \frac{3}{8} =$ ⬚

⬚ 1
(6 marks)

2 Answer these, giving your answers as mixed numbers or fractions.

a) $2\frac{1}{7} + 3\frac{2}{3} =$ ⬚

b) $1\frac{4}{5} - \frac{3}{10} =$ ⬚

c) $3\frac{1}{3} - 2\frac{4}{5} =$ ⬚

d) $4\frac{3}{4} - 3\frac{2}{3} =$ ⬚

⬚ 2
(4 marks)

Using and applying

3 Chloe has this list of fractions: $\frac{3}{8}$ $\frac{3}{10}$ $\frac{5}{12}$ $\frac{1}{3}$ $\frac{7}{12}$ $\frac{5}{8}$

a) She chose two fractions from the list and added them. The total was $\frac{43}{60}$. Find the two fractions she chose.

b) She chose two fractions from the list and found the difference between them. The difference was $\frac{1}{24}$. Find the two fractions she chose.

⬚ 3
(2 marks)

16

4 Some heights of animals are given below.

rhinoceros	lion	elephant	giraffe	gazelle
$1\frac{3}{8}$ m	$1\frac{1}{5}$ m	$3\frac{1}{2}$ m	$4\frac{3}{4}$ m	$\frac{5}{8}$ m

What is the difference in height between:

a) the giraffe and the rhinoceros? **b)** the lion and the gazelle?

c) the elephant and the rhinoceros? **d)** the elephant and the lion?

$\boxed{}$ 4

(4 marks)

5 Complete this addition grid giving answers in their simplest form.

+	$\frac{3}{4}$	$\frac{2}{5}$	$1\frac{3}{8}$	$2\frac{3}{10}$	$3\frac{7}{12}$
$\frac{2}{3}$		$1\frac{1}{15}$		$2\frac{29}{30}$	
$1\frac{3}{4}$	$2\frac{1}{2}$		$3\frac{1}{8}$		$5\frac{1}{3}$

Working out:

$\boxed{}$ 5

(5 marks)

$\boxed{}$ / 21

TOTAL MARKS

Fraction, decimal and percentage equivalents

Checking your understanding

1 Put each set in ascending order.

a) $\frac{3}{10}$, 0.4, 38%

b) $\frac{7}{8}$, 0.88, 85%

c) $\frac{1}{16}$, 0.6, 6%

d) $\frac{6}{15}$, 0.04, 15%

1

(4 marks)

Using and applying

2 There are 25 questions in a test. Jo gets 16 correct, Chloe gets 0.6 of the total number of questions correct and Kim scores 68%.

a) Who scores the most?

b) How many per cent more than Jo does Kim score?

c) How many more questions does Kim get right than Chloe?

2

(3 marks)

3 In a school of 200 children, 45% are girls.
$\frac{4}{9}$ of the girls and $\frac{2}{11}$ of the boys have packed lunches each day.

The rest have school dinners.

a) What percentage of the children in the school have packed lunches?

b) What fraction of the children in the school have school dinners? Write the fraction in its simplest form.

3

(4 marks)

/ 11

TOTAL MARKS

Percentage change

Checking your understanding

1 Calculate these percentage changes. You may use a calculator.

a) Increase 48 by 16%

b) Decrease 64 by 8%

c) Reduce 124 by 32%

d) Increase 12,500 by 74%

1

(4 marks)

Using and applying

2 The number of children in a school decreased by 12% this year. There were 175 children last year. How many children are there this year?

2

(2 marks)

3 In a sale a coat is reduced from £67 by 48%. What is its sale price?

3

(2 marks)

4 The population of a country increased by 3% in 5 years. Its population had been 9 million. What was its population after 5 years?

4

(2 marks)

5 A company's profits increased by 5% between 2010 and 2011. The profits then rose by a further 2% between 2011 and 2012. Their profits for 2010 were £45,000. What are their profits in 2012?

5

(3 marks)

/ 13

TOTAL MARKS

19

Writing a number as a fraction or percentage of another

Checking your understanding

1 **a)** What percentage of 150 is 30?

b) Express 64 as a percentage of 80.

c) What fraction of 280 is 40?

(3 marks) 1

2 **a)** 125 is increased by 50. What percentage increase is this?

b) 350 is decreased by 70. What percentage decrease is this?

(2 marks) 2

3 **a)** Jo adds a number to 125 to get 200. By what percentage has 125 been increased?

b) Jo subtracts a number from 125 to get 30. By what percentage has 125 been decreased?

(2 marks) 3

Using and applying

4 A phone is reduced by £15 in a sale. It now costs £60. By what percentage of the original price was it reduced?

(2 marks) 4

5 Mr Jones got a pay rise of £600. His **new** salary is £15,600 per year.

a) By what fraction of his old salary did it rise?

5

(2 marks)

b) What percentage increase is this?

6 Mrs Jennings weighed 96 kg when she started a diet. By the end of her diet she weighed 78 kg. What percentage of her weight did she lose (to 1dp)?

6

(2 marks)

7 A house's value was £160,000 in 2008 and £220,000 in 2012. By what percentage of its 2008 value had it increased by 2012?

7

(2 marks)

8 Each square in the maps below represents 1 km². The two maps show the approximate surface areas of a lake in 2000 and in 2005, shaded blue.

2000   2005

By what percentage of the lake's area in 2000 has it decreased by 2005? Give your answer to 1 decimal place.

8

(2 marks)

/ 17

TOTAL MARKS

Using ratios to divide amounts

Checking your understanding

(1) Split £36 into the ratio 3:1.

1
(1 mark)

(2) Split £300 into the ratio 5:2:3.

2
(1 mark)

(3) Split £420 into the ratio 3:4:7.

3
(1 mark)

Using and applying

(4) Shade some of the 32 squares in the grid below so that the ratio of grey to white squares is 5:3.

4
(1 mark)

(5) A boss wants to split £640 between three of his workers, Donny, Ronnie and Jonny, in the ratio 1:3:4. How much will they each get?

5
(1 mark)

(6) In a cement mix Dave uses 2 parts cement to 5 parts sand. He wants to make 56kg of mix. How much sand and cement must he use?

Working out:

6
(2 marks)

(7) At the Olympics, the ratio of a country's medals is 2:3:9 (gold : silver : bronze). If the country won 98 medals in total, how many were gold, silver and bronze?

Working out:

7
(2 marks)

/ 9

TOTAL MARKS

Proportional reasoning

Checking your understanding

1 **a)** Eight ice creams cost £9.60.
What is the cost of 5 ice creams?

b) If 3 cans of cola cost £1.29, find the cost of 5 cans.

c) If 5 pens cost £3.45 find the cost of 12 pens.

d) A line of 4 tiles measures 2.76 m.
What would 5 tiles in a line measure?

e) If 3 cans weigh 1035 g, what do 7 cans weigh?

1
(5 marks)

Using and applying

2 A cutlery factory has a machine that takes 16 minutes to make
608 forks. At this rate, how many would it make in 1 hour?

2
(2 marks)

3 A recipe for 12 cakes uses 920 g of flour. How much flour would
be needed for making 9 of these cakes?

3
(2 marks)

4 A runner jogs at a constant rate for 72 minutes. If he ran 10.8 km
in that time, how far had he run after 17 minutes?

4
(2 marks)

5 At today's exchange rate, £70 is equivalent to €87.38 (euros). If
a bottle of perfume costs £24 what would it cost in euros at this
exchange rate? Give your answer to 2 decimal places.

5
(2 marks)

/ 13

TOTAL MARKS

Adding and subtracting negative numbers

Checking your understanding

1   **a)** 5 + −6 = ☐   **b)** 5 − −6 = ☐   **c)** −5 − −6 = ☐

    d) −5 + −6 = ☐   **e)** 2 − −1 = ☐   **f)** −2 − −1 = ☐

    g) 2 + −1 = ☐   **h)** −2 + −1 = ☐   **i)** 10 + −4 = ☐

    j) −10 − −4 = ☐   **k)** 10 − −4 = ☐   **l)** −10 + −4 = ☐

☐ 1
(3 marks)

Using and applying

2   **a)** Add −5 and −9. ☐

    b) Subtract 6 from −2. ☐

    c) Find the total of 3 and −7. ☐

    d) Subtract −3 from 0. ☐

    e) Find the difference between −6 and 6. ☐

☐ 2
(5 marks)

3   Two numbers have a total of −1. One of the numbers is 6. What is the other number?

☐ 3
(1 mark)

4   Two negative integers have a difference of 6. One of the numbers is −2. What is the other number?

☐ 4
(1 mark)

5   The sum of two numbers is −2. The difference is 8. Find the two numbers.

☐ 5
(2 marks)

☐ / 12

TOTAL MARKS

Using formulae

Checking your understanding

1 a) If $P = 2R + 1$, find the value of P when R is 7.

b) If $T = 3S - 4$, find the value of T when S is 3.

c) If $y = 7 - 3x$, find the value of y when x is 2.

1
(3 marks)

Using and applying

2 Use the formula $F = (9C \div 5) + 32$ to find each temperature in degrees Fahrenheit, rounding your answer where necessary.

a) 30° Celsius

b) 5° Celsius

c) 22° Celsius

d) 17° Celsius

2
(4 marks)

3 Use the formula $S = D \div T$, where S is the speed, D is the distance and T is the time.

a) Find the value of S (in km/hour) when D is 51 km and T is 6 hours.

3a
(1 mark)

b) Find the value of D (in km) when S is 10 km/hour and T is 3 hours.

3b
(2 marks)

c) Find the value of T (in hours) when S is 4 km/hour and D is 20 km.

3c
(2 marks)

/ 12

TOTAL MARKS

25

Trial and improvement

Checking your understanding

1 Solve $x^2 - x + 5 = 13$. Give your answer to 1 decimal place. You may find this table helpful

If $x =$	then $x^2 - x + 5$ equals	which is

$x =$

2 Solve $x^2 + 5x = 184.2$. Give your answer to 1 decimal place. You may find this table helpful.

If $x =$	then $x^2 + (5 \times x)$ equals	which is

$x =$

3 Solve $x^3 + x - 1.5 = 331$. Give your answer to 1 decimal place.
Draw a table that starts like this …

If x =	then x³ + x − 1.5 equals	which is

x =

3

(2 marks)

Using and applying

4 Karl knows that the volume of a cuboid is **123.84 cm³**. He knows that the height is 4 cm, and that the length is **5 cm greater** than the width.

Karl writes this equation to show the volume of the cuboid: $x(x + 5) \times 4 = 123.84$

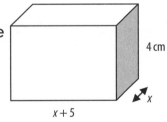

4 cm

x + 5

x

Find the value of x.
You may find this table helpful.

If x =	then x (x + 5) × 4 equals	which is

x =   cm

4

(2 marks)

/ 8

TOTAL MARKS

Solving simple linear equations

Checking your understanding

1 Solve these linear equations.

a) $2y + 5 = 17$ What is the value of y?

b) $5r - 9 = 31$ What is the value of r?

c) $4n - 14 = -2$ What is the value of n?

d) $41 = 7m + 6$ What is the value of m?

e) $9 + 14q = 23$ What is the value of q?

1
(5 marks)

2 Solve these linear equations with unknowns on each side of the equals sign.

a) $6x - 17 = x + 3$ What is the value of x?

b) $7y - 11 = y + 1$ What is the value of y?

c) $6m + 4 = 9m - 17$ What is the value of m?

2
(8 marks)

d) $6g - 4 = 20 - 2g$ What is the value of g?

Using and applying

3 The interior angles of a triangle have a total of 180°.
The interior angles of a triangle are $a°$, $(a + 16)°$ and $(2a)°$

Write an equation to show the total of these three angles equal to 180° and solve it to find the value of a and thus the sizes of the three angles.

Working out:

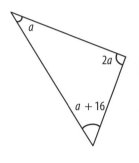

4 Two expressions have been given for opposite sides of each rectangle in centimetres. Use them to find the value of the letter and give the length of the sides.

a)

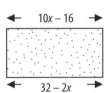

$10x - 16$

$32 - 2x$

b)

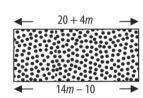

$20 + 4m$

$14m - 10$

c)

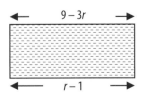

$9 - 3r$

$r - 1$

d)

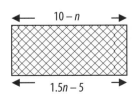

$10 - n$

$1.5n - 5$

Expanding brackets

Checking your understanding

1 Expand each of the following expressions.

a) $3(y - 5)$

b) $3(4 + 2m)$

c) $3(y + z)$

d) $8(2a + b)$

e) $4(2m - 6)$

f) $4(7 - 3n)$

1

(6 marks)

2 Solve each of these expressions by expanding the brackets first.

a) $2(m + 3) = 20$

b) $6(2y - 4) = 36$

2

(4 marks)

Using and applying

3 Write an equation to show the total area of the two rectangles below. The total area of both rectangles is $63\,cm^2$. Solve the equations to find the value of x and work out the area of each of the rectangles.

$x + 6$

3

$2x - 4$

5

3

(1 mark)

Working out:

/ 11

TOTAL MARKS

30

Calculating percentages of amounts (page 9)

1. a) 180 b) 48 c) 4900 d) 246
2. a) 21,526 b) 6528 c) 8910 d) 32,760
3. a) 1326 b) £74,800
4. £5265
5. 48p (allow 1 mark for including £2.72 in working but incorrect answer)

Negative numbers (page 10)

1. a) −6 b) −3 c) −5 d) −8 e) 6 f) −8
2. a) 9°C b) 17°C c) 11°C d) 8°C e) −3°C
3. −14°C
4. 5°C
5. −19°C (allow 1 mark for evidence of correct working but incorrect answer)

Long division (page 11)

1. a) 59 b) 39 c) 16.5 or 16 r 21 d) 11.2 or 11 r 17
2. 153 (2 marks; allow 1 mark for evidence of correct working but incorrect answer)
3. £53,975 (2 marks; allow 1 mark for evidence of correct working but incorrect answer)
4. 6 days (3 marks; allow 2 marks for including 144 hours but not giving the answer in days, allow 1 mark for evidence of correct working but incorrect answer)

Multiplying and dividing decimals (page 12)

1. a) 17.68 b) 4.968 c) 9.686 d) 139.88
2. a) 14.15 b) 20.5 c) 1.3 d) 1.57
3. £17.35 (allow 1 mark for evidence of correct working but incorrect answer)
4. 22.23 cm² (allow 1 mark for evidence of correct working but incorrect answer or if answer does not include cm²)
5. 58.8 km/hour (allow 1 mark for evidence of correct working but incorrect answer or if answer does not include km/hour, km/hr or km per hour)

Formulae (page 13)

1. a) $A = \frac{1}{2}N - 5$ or $A = \frac{N}{2} - 5$
   b) $A = 3N + 7$
   c) $A = 6(N - 2)$ or $A = (N - 2) \times 6$ (brackets must be included or answer given as A = 6N − 12)
   d) $A = \frac{N + 4}{3}$ or $A = (N + 4) \div 3$ or $A = \frac{1}{3}(N + 4)$

2. a) $T = 3 + 4N$ or $T = 4N + 3$ b) £35
3. a) $S = \frac{D}{T}$ b) 39 km/hour
4. a) $D = S \times T$ b) 128 km

Ratio and proportion (page 14)

1. a) 1:3 b) 2:5 c) 3:7 d) 4:7 e) 3:7 f) 6:7
2. a) 2:3 b) $\frac{2}{5}$
3. a) 9:10 b) 16 boys
4. 9:7:5
5. a) 6 b) 8 c) 10 d) 3:4:5

Areas and perimeters of rectangles (page 15)

1. a) 26 cm, 36 cm² b) 28 cm, 33 cm² c) 29 cm, 49.5 cm² d) 11 cm, 7.5 cm²
2. 5 cm and 3 cm (allow 1 mark for evidence of correct working but incorrect answer)
3. £18 (allow 1 mark for including 15 in working but incorrect answer)
4. 2.5 m (no mark for the answer 40, allow 1 mark for answer 0.025 or an answer without a unit of measurement given)

Adding and subtracting fractions and mixed numbers (pages 16–17)

1. (Equivalent fractions for these are acceptable) a) $\frac{13}{15}$ b) $\frac{1}{8}$ c) $1\frac{2}{45}$ or $\frac{47}{45}$ d) $\frac{11}{24}$ e) $\frac{18}{35}$ f) $\frac{37}{56}$
2. a) $5\frac{17}{21}$ or $\frac{122}{21}$ b) $1\frac{1}{2}$ or $\frac{3}{2}$ c) $\frac{8}{15}$ d) $1\frac{1}{12}$ or $\frac{13}{12}$
3. a) $\frac{5}{12} + \frac{3}{10}$ b) $\frac{5}{8} - \frac{7}{12}$
4. a) $3\frac{3}{8}$ m or $\frac{27}{8}$ m b) $\frac{23}{40}$ m c) $2\frac{1}{8}$ m or $\frac{17}{8}$ m d) $2\frac{3}{10}$ m or $\frac{23}{10}$ m
5. (Award 1 mark for each correct answer)

+	$\frac{3}{4}$	$\frac{2}{5}$	$1\frac{3}{8}$	$2\frac{3}{10}$	$3\frac{7}{12}$
$\frac{2}{3}$	$1\frac{5}{12}$	$1\frac{1}{15}$	$2\frac{1}{24}$	$2\frac{29}{30}$	$4\frac{1}{4}$
$1\frac{3}{4}$	$2\frac{1}{2}$	$2\frac{3}{20}$	$3\frac{1}{8}$	$4\frac{1}{20}$	$5\frac{1}{3}$

Fraction, decimal and percentage equivalents (page 18)

1. a) $\frac{3}{10}$, 38%, 0.4 b) 85%, $\frac{7}{8}$, 0.88 c) 6%, $\frac{1}{16}$, 0.6 d) 0.04, 15%, $\frac{6}{15}$
2. (Jo scored $\frac{16}{25}$ = 64%, Chloe scored $\frac{15}{25}$ = 60% and Kim scored $\frac{17}{25}$ = 68%) a) Kim b) 4% c) 2 questions
3. a) 30% have packed lunches (allow 1 mark for evidence of correct working but incorrect answer) b) $\frac{7}{10}$ (allow 1 mark for evidence of correct working but incorrect answer)

Percentage change (page 19)

1. a) 55.68 b) 58.88 c) 84.32 d) 21,750
2. 154 children (allow 1 mark for including 21 in working but incorrect answer)
3. £34.84 (pound sign must be included for the full 2 marks; allow 1 mark for including 32.16 in working but incorrect answer)
4. 9.27 million or 9,270,000 (allow 1 mark for including 0.27 or 270,000 in working but incorrect answer)
5. £48,195 (pound sign must be included for the full 3 marks; allow 1 mark only for £48,150 as this shows that the two percentages were combined first. This is not correct as first 5% must be calculated and then 2% OF THE NEW TOTAL. Allow 1 mark for including £2250 in working and a second mark for including £945 in working but incorrect answer)

Writing a number as a fraction or percentage of another (pages 20–21)

1. a) 20% b) 80% c) $\frac{1}{7}$
2. a) 40% b) 20%
3. a) 60% b) 76%
4. 20% (allow 1 mark for evidence of correct working but incorrect answer)
5. a) $\frac{600}{15000}$ or $\frac{1}{25}$ b) 4%
6. 18.8% (allow 1 mark for evidence of correct working but incorrect answer)
7. 37.5% (allow 1 mark for evidence of correct working but incorrect answer)
8. 64.3% (allow 1 mark for an incorrectly rounded answer, e.g. 64.2857)

Using ratios to divide amounts (page 22)

1. £27 and £9
2. £150, £60 and £90
3. £90, £120, £210
4. Exactly 20 grey squares must be shaded.
5. £80, £240, £320
6. 16 kg cement and 40 kg sand (allow 1 mark if answers are given the wrong way around)
7. 14 gold, 21 silver and 63 bronze (allow 1 mark for including 7 in working but incorrect answer)

Proportional reasoning (page 23)

1. a) £6 b) £2.15 c) £8.28 d) 3.45 m
   e) 2415 g or 2.415 kg
   . 2280 (allow 1 mark for including 38 in working but incorrect answer)
3. 690 g (unit of measurement must be included for the full 2 marks; allow 1 mark for given a decimal answer, e.g. 689.4 or the answer 689 g)
4. 2.55 km (unit of measurement must be included for the full 2 marks)
5. €29.96 (euros must be included in answer for the full 2 marks; allow 1 mark if not correctly rounded to 2 decimal places, e.g. 30 or 29.95)

Adding and subtracting negative numbers (page 24)

1. a) −1 b) 11 c) 1 d) −11 e) 3 f) −1
   g) 1 h) −3 i) 6 j) −6 k) 14 l) −14 (allow 1 mark for each correct row of answers)
2. a) −14 b) −8 c) −4 d) −3 e) 12
3. −7
4. −8
5. −5 and 3 (allow 1 mark for two numbers that have either a sum of −2 or a difference of 8 but not both)

Using formulae (page 25)

1. a) 15 b) 5 c) 1
2. a) 86°F b) 41°F c) 71.6°F or 72°F
   d) 62.6°F or 63°F
3. a) 8.5 km/hour b) 30 km (allow 1 mark for evidence of correct working but incorrect answer)
   c) 5 hours (allow 1 mark for evidence of correct working but incorrect answer)

Trial and improvement (pages 26–27)

1. $x = 3.4$ (2 marks; allow 1 mark for a partially completed table with some correct substitutions but incorrect answer)
2. $x = 11.3$ (allow 1 mark for a partially completed table with some correct substitutions but incorrect answer)
3. $x = 6.9$ (allow 1 mark for a partially completed table with some correct substitutions but incorrect answer)
4. $x = 3.6$ cm (allow 1 mark for a partially completed table with some correct substitutions but incorrect answer)

Solving simple linear equations (pages 28–29)

1. a) 6 b) 8 c) 3 d) 5 e) 1
2. a) 4 b) 2 c) 7 d) 3 (each part worth 2 marks; allow 1 mark for evidence of correct working but incorrect answer)
3. $4a + 16 = 180$, $a = 41$ and angles are 41°, 82°, 57° (allow 1 mark for giving correct value of a but without giving angles)
4. a) $x = 4$ and sides are 24 units (allow 1 mark for writing $10x − 16 = 32 − 2x$ and trying to solve it but incorrect answer)
   b) $m = 3$ and sides are 32 units (allow 1 mark for writing $20 + 4m = 14m − 10$ and trying to solve it but incorrect answer)
   c) $r = 2.5$ and sides are 1.5 units (allow 1 mark for writing $9 − 3r = r − 1$ and trying to solve it but incorrect answer)
   d) $n = 6$ and sides are 4 units (allow 1 mark for writing $10 − n = 1.5n − 5$ and trying to solve it but incorrect answer)

Expanding brackets (page 30)

1. a) $3y − 15$ b) $12 + 6m$ c) $3y + 3z$
   d) $16a + 8b$ e) $8m − 24$ f) $28 − 12n$
2. a) $m = 7$ (allow 1 mark for evidence of correct working but incorrect answer)
   b) $y = 5$ (allow 1 mark for evidence of correct working but incorrect answer)
3. $x = 5$, areas = 33 cm² and 30 cm²

Finding a rule for the nth term of a sequence (page 31)

1. a) 18, 21, 24, 27, 30 b) 19, 22, 25, 28, 31 c) 16, 19, 22, 25, 28
2. a) $4n$ b) $4n + 2$ c) $5n$ d) $5n − 1$
   e) $10n − 3$
3. a) $3n + 2$ b) The 2 grey squares as you go from shape to shape in the sequence represent the +2 in the rule. The 3 'legs' of each shape grow as you go from shape to shape in the sequence and represent the 3n. c) 32

Drawing straight line graphs (pages 32–33)

1. a)   b)

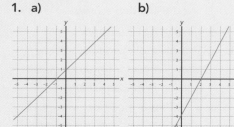

2.

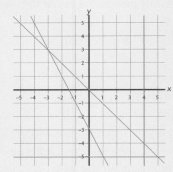

3. Circled $y = −2x$, $y = 3x$, $y = −4x$, $y = \frac{1}{2}x$ (allow 1 mark if one has been missed or if one other has been incorrectly circled)
4. $y = x + 3$, $y = −2x + 3$, $y = 3$, $y = \frac{1}{2}x + 3$ (allow 1 mark if one has been missed or if one other has been incorrectly circled)
5. (award up to 2 marks for clear explanations that include the main points of the following):
   a) This could not be the line as the equation has a negative gradient and so would slope up to the left rather than the right.
   b) This could not be the line as the equation has +4 which means that the intercept with the y-axis should be at +4 which is above the x-axis, not below it.
   c) This could be the line as it has a positive gradient and a negative value for the intercept with the y-axis.

Describing straight line graphs (pages 34–35)

1. (2 marks for each part; award 1 mark for the correct gradient and 1 for the correct intercept)
   a) $y = x + 1$ (accept $y = 1x + 1$)
   b) $y = 3x − 2$ c) $y = \frac{1}{2}x$ d) $y = −2x + 1$
2. a) $y = 7$
   b) $y = x + 3$ (award 1 mark for correct gradient and 1 for correct intercept)
   c) A line drawn on the graph that slopes up to the left and passes through both (0, 10) and (10, 0).
3. a) $y = 2x + 2$ b) $y = −x$

Plans and elevations (page 36)
(2 marks for each question; allow 1 mark each for plan and elevation)

1. a)

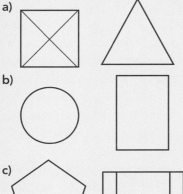

   b)

   c)

Elevation could also look like this:

2. Plan and elevation: the shapes, position and orientation of the triangle and rectangles may differ but may be acceptable.

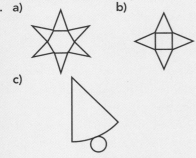

Nets and 2-D representations of 3-D shapes (page 37)

1. a)   b)

   c)

2. Four shapes should be circled.

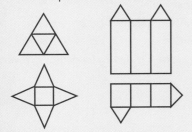

Quadrilaterals (pages 38–39)

1. a) parallelogram b) kite c) trapezium d) rhombus e) rectangle f) trapezium (sometimes also called an isosceles trapezium).

2. a) false (a rhombus also has equal sides) b) true c) false (it can contain one or two) d) true e) false

3. 2, 2, 4
   2, 2, 0
   2, 2, 0
   1, 0, 2 (*1 mark for each correct line*)

4. a) The diagonals of a square are always equal. b) The diagonals of a kite are never equal. c) The diagonals of a trapezium are sometimes equal. d) The diagonals of a rhombus always cross at their midpoints. e) The diagonals of a rectangle always cross at their midpoints.

Angles of polygons (pages 40–41)

1. 360°
2. a) 60° b) 72° c) 45° d) 36°
3. a) 124° b) 66°
4. a) 45° b) 125° c) 70° d) 135°
5. Exterior angles are 120°, 50°, g°, 75° and 40° so g must be 75°.
6. Each exterior angle of a regular 12-sided shape is 360 ÷ 12 = 30° so each interior angle must be 150° (*allow 1 mark for evidence of correct working but incorrect answer*)
7. a) 180°, 360°, 540°, 720°, 900°, 1,080°, 1260°, 1440° (*allow ½ mark for each correct answer*)
   b) Divide 360 by 12 to find the value of each of the exterior angles of the polygon. Then subtract this answer (*30*) from 180 (angles on a straight line) to find an interior angle (150) and then multiply by 12 to find the sum 150 × 12 = 1800 (*allow 1 mark for some of this explanation but not all*)
   c) 3240° (*allow 1 mark for evidence of correct working but incorrect answer*)

Angles between lines (pages 42–43)

1. a) $a = 67°$ b) $b = 41°$ c) $c = 60°$
   d) $d = 123°$
2. $e = 100°$ $f = 75°$
3. $a = 145°$ (*allow 1 or 2 marks for working that shows some of the following aspects*): Angle at R must be 35° (using angles of a triangle), both angles at S must be right angles 90°, angle at T (not angle a) must be 35° (using angles of a triangle) or using knowledge that angles in a quadrilateral add to 360°.
4. (*Allow up to 3 marks for including the following aspects*):
   A trapezium has a set of parallel lines (these could be marked on the diagram), the other interior angles of the trapezium must be 70° (using angles on a straight line) and 110° (alternate angles), so n must be 360° – 70° – 110° – 40° = 140°.

Areas of shapes made from rectangles (page 44)

1. a) 42 cm² b) 66 cm² c) 98 cm² d) 78 cm² e) 120 cm² f) 140 cm²
2. a) 80.25 cm² (*allow 1 mark or 2 marks for including 118.75 or 38.5 in working and attempting subtraction but incorrect answer*)
   b) 104 cm² (*allow 1 mark for a subtraction method including 144.5 or an addition method including 38.5, 35.75 and / or 29.75 in working but incorrect answer*)

The circumference of a circle (page 45)

1. a) 18.8 cm b) 25.1 cm c) 31.4 cm d) 20.1 cm e) 28.3 cm f) 29.8 cm
2. a) 6.2 cm (*allow 1 mark for an attempt to divide 19.5 by pi but incorrect answer*)
   b) 6.7 cm (*allow 1 mark for an attempt to divide 42.1 by pi and dividing by 2 but incorrect answer*)
3. 11.6 cm (*allow 1 mark for evidence of correct working but incorrect answer*)

The area of a circle (page 46)

1. a) 28.3 cm² b) 50.3 cm² c) 78.5 cm² d) 32.2 cm² e) 63.6 cm² f) 70.9 cm²
2. a) 2.5 cm (*allow 1 mark for an attempt to divide 19.5 by pi and then find the square root but incorrect answer*)
   b) 7.3 cm (*allow 1 mark for an attempt to divide 19.5 by pi and then find the square root but incorrect answer*)
3. 21.5 cm² (*allow up to 2 marks for subtracting the area of the circle from 100 (the area of the square) but incorrect answer*)

The volume of a cuboid (page 47)

1. a) 360 cm³ b) 420 cm³ c) 1080 cm³
2. (*2 marks for each part; allow 1 mark*

for evidence of correct working but incorrect answer) **a)** 6 cm **b)** 20 cm

Transformations (page 48)

1. *(2 marks for each part; allow 1 mark for one error in rotation or reflection but otherwise correct)*

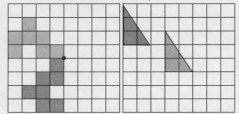

2. *(half mark for each part)* **a)** true **b)** true **c)** false **d)** true **e)** true **f)** false **g)** true **h)** false **i)** true **j)** false **k)** true **l)** false

Enlarging shapes (page 49)

1. *(2 marks for each part; allow 1 mark for one error in enlargement but otherwise correct)*

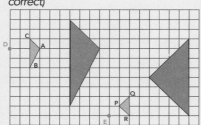

2. The second set should be circled, with an explanation that if the origin is the centre of enlargement then the x and y coordinates will all be 5 times larger for the scale factor 5 *(allow 1 mark for correct but explanation not clear or detailed enough)*

Frequency diagrams (pages 50–51)

1. **a)** The table should show class intervals $120 \leq B < 140$ and $140 \leq B < 160$ and the following frequencies: 7, 12, 24, 7 *(4 marks for correct table, subtract 1 mark for each error)*

   b) *(4 marks for correct table, subtract 1 mark for each error)*

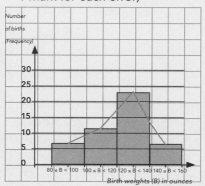

2. The third diagram showing the frequencies 6, 9 and 5 should be ticked. The explanation should show

that the child has organised the data given into equal groups with those frequencies *(allow 1 mark for correct answer but explanation not clear or detailed enough)*

Scatter graphs (pages 52–53)

1. **a)**

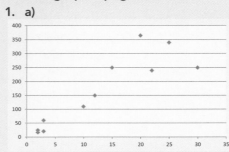

   b) It shows some evidence of positive correlation, for example the longer the lifespan of an animal then the longer the pregnancy. There are not many items of data, however, which could suggest that the conclusions are less reliable than with a greater number of items.

2. **a)** Negative correlation – it suggests that the higher your level of fitness the shorter the length of time to run 10 km. **b)** Zero or no correlation – it suggests there is no relationship between maths test score and the time it takes to run 10 km. **c)** Positive correlation – it suggests that the higher your body weight, the longer the length of time to run 10 km.

Pie charts (page 54)

1. *(half mark for each correct angle)* 126°, 54°, 79.2° or 79°, 50.4° or 50°, 39.6° or 40°, 10.8° or 11°

2. Pie chart where angles of each section are 126°, 54°, 79°, 50°, 40°, 11°. The pie chart should be correctly labelled with a title.

Probability – outcomes (page 55)

1. H1, H2, H3, H4, H5, H6, T1, T2, T3, T4, T5, T6

2. *(allow 1 mark for drawing a tree diagram with the correct number of branches but unlabelled; allow 2 marks for labelled tree diagram with one error)*

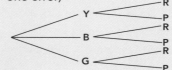

3. **a)** true **b)** true **c)** false

Mutually exclusive events (page 56)

1. $\frac{10}{11}$ 2. $\frac{1}{2}$ 3. $\frac{12}{13}$ 4. 0.3

5. **a)** 0.35 *(allow 1 mark for evidence of subtracting decimals from 1 with incorrect answer)* **b)** 0.8 *(allow 1 mark for evidence of subtracting 0.2 with incorrect answer)* **c)** 90 *(allow 1 mark for evidence of multiplying 0.3 by 300 from 1 with incorrect answer)*

Using and applying maths (pages 57–59)

1. **a)** £19 **b)** 25% (note it is NOT 20%, as 20% of £80 is £16)

2. *(2 marks for each part; allow 1 mark for less simplified expression)*
   a) $2(s + t)$ **b)** $4(s + t) - s$ or $3s + 4t$
   c) $6s + 4t$ or $2(3s + 2t)$ **d)** $5s + 6t$

3. **a)** 18 **b)** 8 **c)** 42

4. **a)** 36 **b)** 0.5 or $\frac{1}{2}$

5. **a)** $4y + 8 = 48$ so $y = 10$ **b)** $4b + 16 = 52$ so $b = 9$ **c)** $8t + 10 = 66$ so $t = 7$

6. For eyes $2x + 2y = 30$, for legs $2x = 20$, so there must be 10 people and 5 fish *(allow 1 mark for evidence of appropriate working but incorrect answer)*

7. **a)** $2x + 8$ **b)** $x^2 + 2x$ **c)** $6x + 9$

8. **a)** $m = 30x + 20$ **b)** $m = 70x + 35$
   c) $m = 40x + 20$ **d)** $m = 50x$

9. 18.6 cm *(allow 1 mark for incorrect rounding or not giving unit, e.g. 19 cm or 18.6)*

10. 18 sides *(2 marks; allow 1 mark for attempting to divide 360 by 20 with incorrect answer)*

11. 12 sides *(allow 1 mark for subtracting 150 from 180 and attempting to divide 360 by 30 with incorrect answer)*

12. 339 cm² *(allow 1 or 2 marks for evidence of (12 × 3.142) – (6 × 3.142) included but with incorrect answer)*

Finding a rule for the nth term of a sequence

Checking your understanding

1 Continue the sequence for each rule given for the nth term of a sequence.

a) $3n$ 3, 6, 9, 12, 15, …

b) $3n + 1$ 4, 7, 10, 13, 16, …

c) $3n - 2$ 1, 4, 7, 10, 13, …

1 (3 marks)

2 Write a rule for the nth term of each sequence.

a) 4, 8, 12, 16, 20, 24, 28, …

b) 6, 10, 14, 18, 22, 26, 30, …

c) 5, 10, 15, 20, 25, 30, 35, 40, …

d) 4, 9, 14, 19, 24, 29, 34, 39, …

e) 7, 17, 27, 37, 47, 57, 67, 77, …

2 (5 marks)

Using and applying

3 Here is a sequence of shapes made from white and grey squares.

 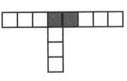 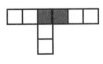 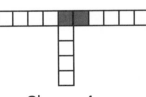

Shape 1   Shape 2   Shape 3   Shape 4

a) Find how many squares in each shape and write a rule for the nth term of each sequence.

3 (3 marks)

b) In your own words, explain how the grey and white squares are linked to your rule.

c) How many squares in total will be in shape 10?

/ 11

TOTAL MARKS

31

Drawing straight line graphs

Checking your understanding

1 **a)** Draw the line $y = x + 1$.

b) Draw the line $y = 2x - 4$.

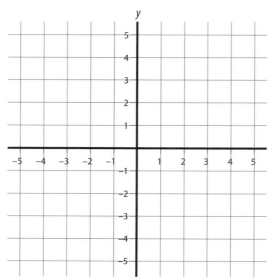

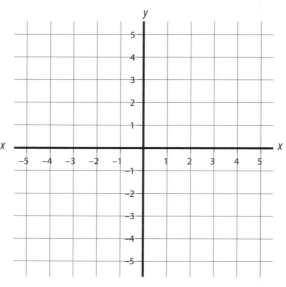

1

(2 marks)

2 Plot these lines on the same graph.

a) $y = -2x - 3$

b) $y = -5$

c) $x = 4$

d) $y = -x$

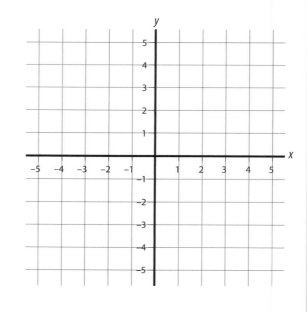

2

(4 marks)

Using and applying

3 Circle each of the equations below that, when plotted as a graph, will pass through the origin.

$y = -2x$ $y = -4$ $y = 2x + 1$ $y = 3x$

$y = x - 4$ $y = -2x + 6$ $y = -4x$ $y = \frac{1}{2}x$

3

(2 marks)

4 Circle each of the equations below that, when plotted as a graph, will pass through the point (0, 3).

$x = 3$ $y = x + 3$ $y = -2x + 3$ $y = 3x - 3$

$y = 3$ $y = 3x$ $y = \frac{1}{2}x + 3$ $y = x - 3$

4

(2 marks)

5 The numbers on this coordinate grid are not shown. Say whether each equation given could represent the line shown or not.

Explain your answer in words.

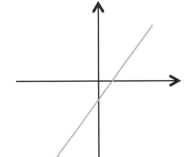

a) $y = -x - 4$

b) $y = x + 4$

5

(6 marks)

c) $y = x - 4$

/ 16

TOTAL MARKS

33

Describing straight line graphs

Checking your understanding

1 Give the equation of each line.

a)

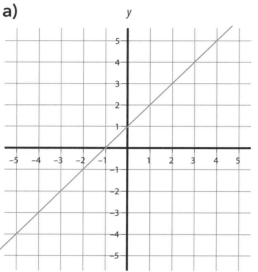

b)

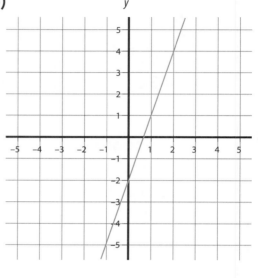

c)

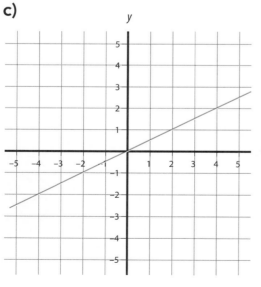

d)

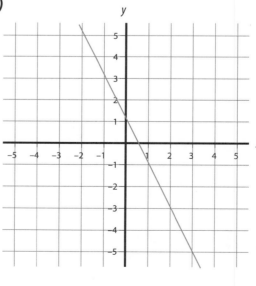

1

(8 marks)

Using and applying

2 Sam has been plotting some lines on a graph. The line AB is parallel to CD.

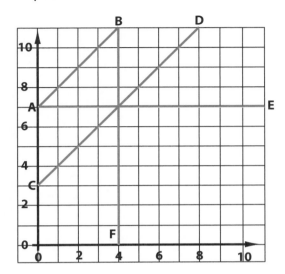

a) The equation of the line BF is $x = 4$.
   What is the equation of the line AE?

2a
(1 mark)

b) The line AB has the equation $y = x + 7$.
   What is the equation of the line CD?

2b
(2 marks)

c) On the graph, draw and label the line GH with the equation
   $y = -x + 10$.

2c
(1 mark)

3 Use each description to work out the equation of each line.

a) The straight line passes through
   the points (1, 4) and (0, 2).

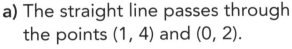

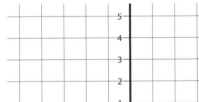

b) The straight line passes through
   the points (4, −4) and (−4, 4).

3
(2 marks)

/ 14

TOTAL MARKS

35

Plans and elevations

Checking your understanding

1 Sketch a plan and an elevation of each shape.

a)

Plan:	Elevation:

b)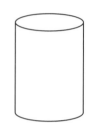

Plan:	Elevation:

1

(6 marks)

c)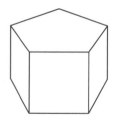

Plan:	Elevation:

Using and applying

2 A cuboid is placed on a flat surface. A triangular prism is placed on top of the cuboid so that one of its triangular faces is in contact with one of the rectangular faces of the cuboid. Sketch a possible plan and an elevation of the two joined shapes.

2

(2 marks)

Plan:	Elevation:

/ 8

TOTAL MARKS

36

Nets and 2-D representations of 3-D shapes

Checking your understanding

1 Sketch a net for each shape.

a)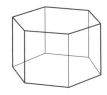

Draw net here:

b)

Draw net here:

c)

Draw net here:

1

(3 marks)

Using and applying

2 Circle all the nets that will **not** form a triangular prism when folded.

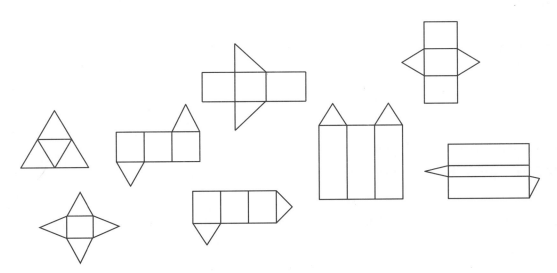

2

(4 marks)

/ 7

TOTAL MARKS

37

Quadrilaterals

Checking your understanding

1 Write the name of each shape as accurately as you can.

a)

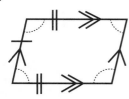

b)

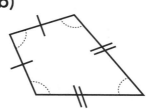

c)

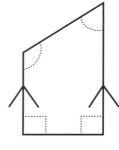

d)

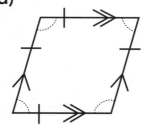

e)

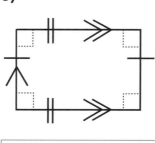

f)

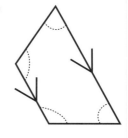

1

(6 marks)

Using and applying

2 True or false?

a) The only quadrilateral that has four equal sides is a square.

b) All trapeziums have one pair of parallel sides.

2

(5 marks)

c) A kite can never contain a right angle.

d) A parallelogram with all equal sides and four right angles is called a square.

e) All trapeziums are symmetrical.

3 Complete the table.

Picture	Number of pairs of parallel sides	Number of pairs of equal sides	Number of right angles
	2		

3

(4 marks)

4 The diagonals of a shape go from corner to corner. Tick the appropriate box for each shape.

a) Square

Diagonals are always equal

Diagonals are sometimes equal

Diagonals are never equal

b) Kite

Diagonals are always equal

Diagonals are sometimes equal

Diagonals are never equal

c) Trapezium

Diagonals are always equal

Diagonals are sometimes equal

Diagonals are never equal

d) Rhombus

Diagonals always cross at their midpoints

Diagonals sometimes cross at their midpoints

Diagonals never cross at their midpoints

e) Rectangle

Diagonals always cross at their midpoints

Diagonals sometimes cross at their midpoints

Diagonals never cross at their midpoints

4

(5 marks)

/ 20

TOTAL MARKS

Angles of polygons

Checking your understanding

1 What is the sum of exterior angles of a polygon?

1

(1 mark)

2 Find one of the exterior angles for each shape.

a) A regular hexagon

b) A regular pentagon

c) A regular octagon

d) A regular decagon

2

(4 marks)

3 **a)** A hexagon has exterior angles of 34°, 36°, 121°, 19°, 26° and *b*°. Find the value of *b*.

b) A pentagon has exterior angles of 73°, 89°, 121°, 11° and *c*°. Find the value of c.

3

(2 marks)

4 An interior or an exterior angle is given in each diagram below. Find the missing angle each time.

a)

b)

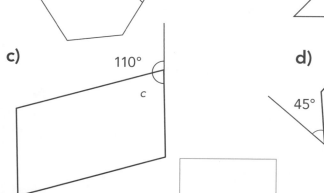

135° *a*

55° *b*

4

(4 marks)

c)

110°

c

d)

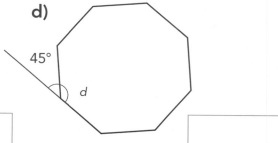

45°

d

40

Using and applying

5 Find the exterior angles of this pentagon. Use your answers to find the size of angle g.

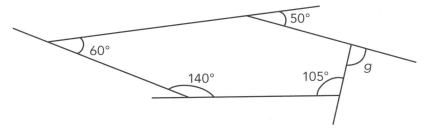

5

(4 marks)

6 Find the size of an interior angle of a regular polygon with 12 sides.

> **Working out:**

6

(2 marks)

7 **a)** Complete this table to show the sum of all the interior angles of each shape.

	Equilateral triangle	Square	Regular pentagon	Regular hexagon	Regular heptagon	Regular octagon	Regular nonagon	Regular decagon
Sum of the interior angles		360°						

7a

(4 marks)

b) Explain in words how you can find the sum of the interior angles of a polygon with 12 sides.

7b

(2 marks)

c) Find the sum of the interior angles of a polygon with 20 sides.

> **Working out:**

7c

(2 marks)

/ 25

TOTAL MARKS

41

Angles between lines

Checking your understanding

1 Find the size of each angle marked with a letter.

a)

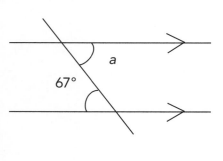

b)

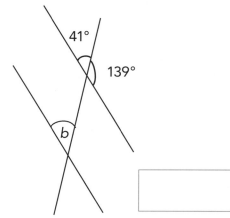

1

(4 marks)

c)

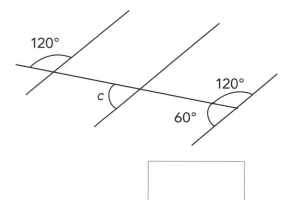

d)

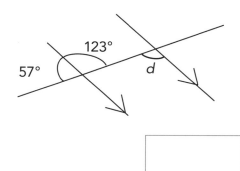

2 Find the size of the angles *e* and *f*.

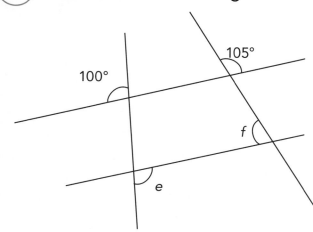

2

(2 marks)

Using and applying

3 This diagram shows triangle PQR. Point S lies on the line PQ and point T lies on the line PR. Line QR is parallel to line ST. Calculate the size of angle *a*.

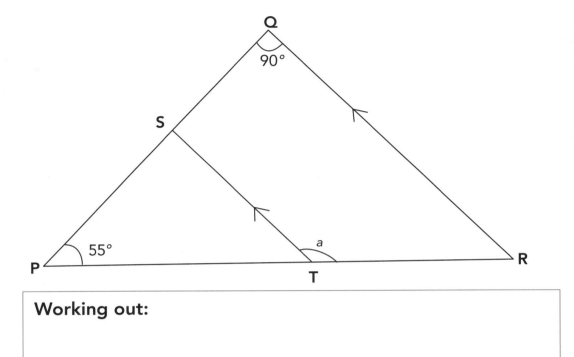

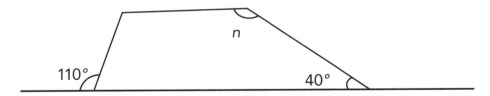

Working out:

Angle *a* =

3
(3 marks)

4 This picture shows the end face of a trapezium prism on a table.

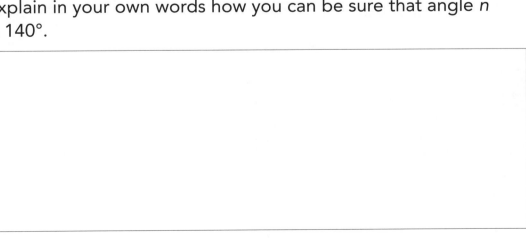

Explain in your own words how you can be sure that angle *n* is 140°.

4
(3 marks)

/ 12

TOTAL MARKS

Areas of shapes made from rectangles

Checking your understanding

1 Find the area of each shape.

a)

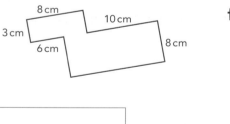

4 cm
3 cm
2 cm
5 cm

b)

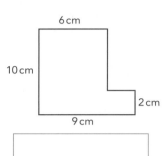

6 cm
10 cm
2 cm
9 cm

c)

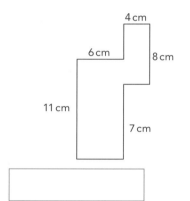

4 cm
6 cm
8 cm
11 cm
7 cm

d)

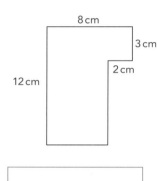

8 cm
3 cm
2 cm
12 cm

1

(6 marks)

e)

8 cm
3 cm
10 cm
6 cm
8 cm

f)

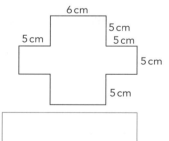

6 cm
5 cm
5 cm
5 cm
5 cm
5 cm

2 Find the area of the shaded region of each shape

a)

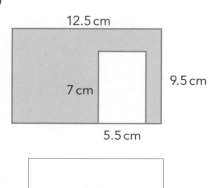

12.5 cm
9.5 cm
7 cm
5.5 cm

b)

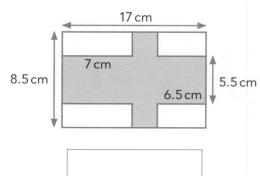

17 cm
8.5 cm
7 cm
5.5 cm
6.5 cm

2

(6 marks)

/ 12

TOTAL MARKS

44

The circumference of a circle

Checking your understanding

1 Find the circumference of each circle. Give your answers to 1 decimal place.

a)

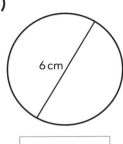

b)

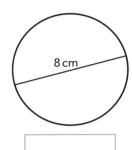

c)

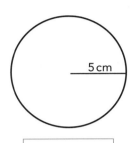

d)

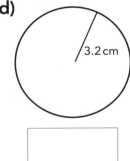

e)

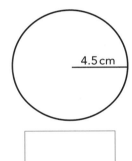

f)

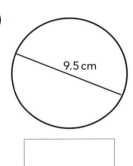

1

(6 marks)

Using and applying

2 a) Find the diameter (to 1 decimal place) of a circle with a circumference of 19.5 cm.

b) Find the radius (to 1 decimal place) of a circle with a circumference of 42.1 cm.

2

(4 marks)

3 A jeweller makes earrings from lengths of wire. This design has two identical circles and their diameters. Calculate the length of wire needed to make this earring (to 1 decimal place).

Each diameter is 1.4 cm

3

(2 marks)

/ 12

TOTAL MARKS

The area of a circle

Checking your understanding

1 Find the area of each circle. Give your answers to 1 decimal place.

a)

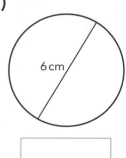

6 cm

b)

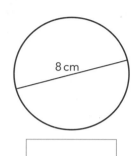

8 cm

c)

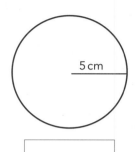

5 cm

d)

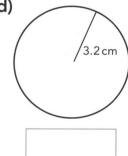

3.2 cm

e)

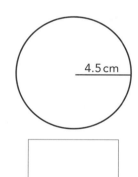

4.5 cm

f)

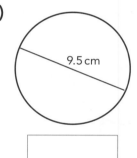

9.5 cm

Using and applying

2 **a)** Find the radius (to 1 decimal place) of a circle with an area of 19.5 cm².

b) Find the diameter (to 1 decimal place) of a circle with an area of 42.1 cm².

3 A circle with a radius of 5 cm fits inside a square so that it touches the perimeter at four points. Find the total area of the shaded regions to 1 decimal place.

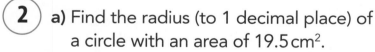
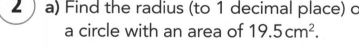

The volume of a cuboid

Checking your understanding

1 Find the volume of these cuboids.

a)

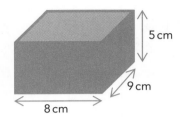

5 cm
9 cm
8 cm

Working out:

Volume =

1a
(1 mark)

b)

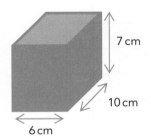

7 cm
10 cm
6 cm

Working out:

Volume =

1b
(1 mark)

c)

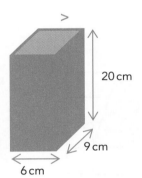

20 cm
9 cm
6 cm

Working out:

Volume =

1c
(1 mark)

Using and applying

2 Find the missing length or height.

a)

? cm
5 cm
8 cm

The volume of this cuboid is 240 cm³

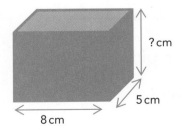

Working out:

Height =

2
(4 marks)

b)

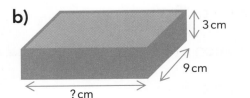

3 cm
9 cm
? cm

The volume of this cuboid is 540 cm³

Working out:

Width =

/ 7

TOTAL MARKS

47

Transformations

Checking your understanding

1 Shade to show the position of each shape after its transformation.

a) 90° rotation anticlockwise about the marked point

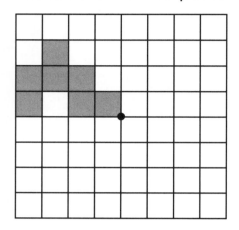

b) translation (–3, 2)

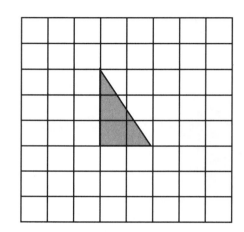

	1
(4 marks)

Using and applying

2 Say whether each statement is true or false.

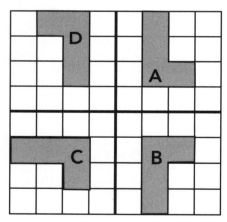

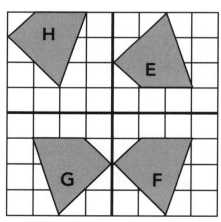

	2
(6 marks)

a) B is a reflection of A [ ]

b) C is a reflection of A [ ]

c) D is a rotation of B [ ]

d) C is a rotation of B [ ]

e) D is a rotation of A [ ]

f) C is a translation of A [ ]

g) F is a reflection of E [ ]

h) G is a rotation of F [ ]

i) G is a rotation of E [ ]

j) H is a rotation of G [ ]

k) H is a translation of F [ ]

l) H is a rotation of E [ ]

	/ 10

TOTAL MARKS

Enlarging shapes

Checking your understanding

1 **a)** Enlarge triangle ABC by a scale factor of 3 using the centre of enlargement D.

b) Enlarge triangle PQR by a scale factor of 4 using the centre of enlargement E.

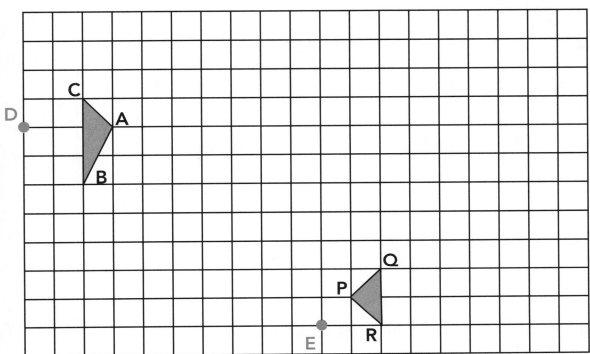

1

(4 marks)

Using and applying

2 A triangle has vertices at the following coordinates: (1, 0), (1, 1) and (3, 1). It is enlarged by a scale factor of 5 using the origin (0, 0) as the centre of enlargement. Circle which of these sets of coordinates show the correct vertices of the enlarged shape.

(5, 0), (1, 5) and (10, 5)   (5, 0), (5, 5) and (10, 5)

(5, 0), (5, 5) and (15, 5)

2

(2 marks)

Explain your answer in words.

/ 6

TOTAL MARKS

49

Frequency diagrams

Checking your understanding

1 This raw data show the birth weights of 50 babies.

Birth weights in ounces:
115, 108, 102, 143, 146, 124, 124, 145, 106, 85,
107, 124, 122, 101, 128, 104, 97, 137, 103, 142,
130, 156, 133, 120, 91, 127, 153, 121, 120, 99,
149, 129, 139, 114, 138, 129, 138, 131, 125, 114,
128, 134, 114, 92, 85, 135, 87, 125, 128, 105

a) Continue the equal class intervals in the table below and complete the table.

Birth weights (B) in ounces	Tally	Frequency
$80 \leq B < 100$		
$100 \leq B < 120$		

1

(8 marks)

b) Plot the information in the table as a frequency diagram / polygon.

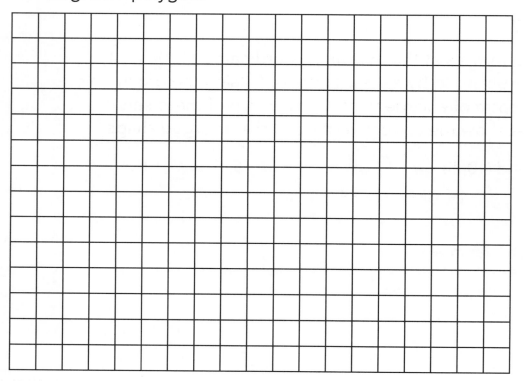

50

Using and applying

2 Twenty students were asked to say how much time they spent revising each week.

The information collected is shown here:

> Number of hours each student said they spent revising:
> 6, 8, 9, 4, 5, 6, 7, 4, 7, 8, 6, 5, 4,
> 7, 8, 9, 7, 4, 6, 7

Tick which of these frequency diagrams shows the information correctly.

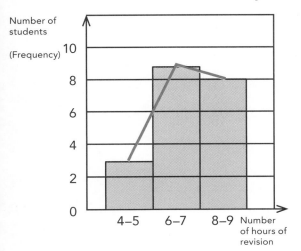

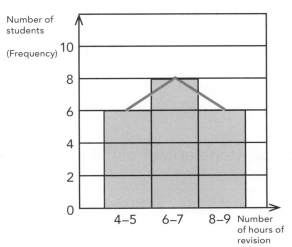

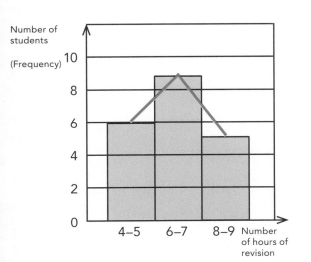

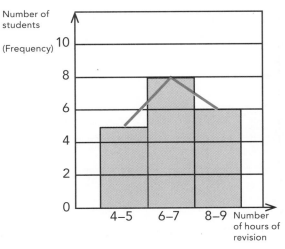

(2 marks)

Explain your answer in words.

/ 10

TOTAL MARKS

Scatter graphs

Checking your understanding

1 This raw data show the typical lifespan (in years) and the length of pregnancy (in days) for a variety of animals.

Animal	Typical lifespan in years	Length of pregnancy in days
Hippo	30	250
Horse	25	340
Lion	10	110
Goat	12	150
Guinea pig	3	60
Hamster	2	17
Rat	3	21
Mouse	2	25
Bear	22	240
Deer	15	250
Donkey	20	365
Sheep	12	150

a) Sketch a scatter diagram of the information.

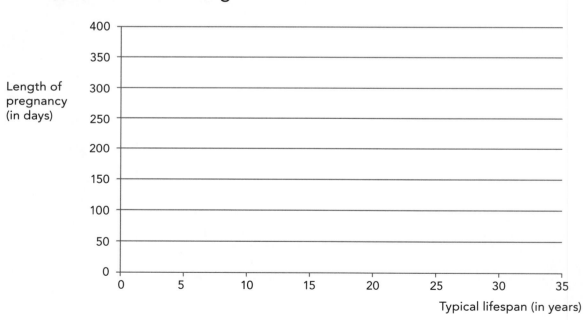

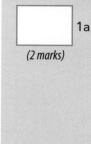

1a

(2 marks)

b) Describe what the scatter graph shows and say whether you think the information is reliable.

1b

(1 mark)

Using and applying

2 Three scatter graphs are shown below. For each graph identify the correlation and explain the relationship that it shows.

a)

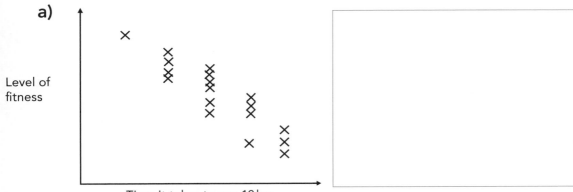

Level of fitness

Time it takes to run 10 km

b)

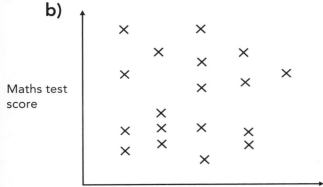

Maths test score

Time it takes to run 10 km

c)

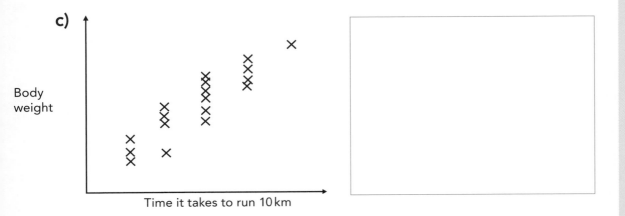

Body weight

Time it takes to run 10 km

2

(6 marks)

/ 9

TOTAL MARKS

53

Pie charts

Checking your understanding

1 This chart shows the activities or items that 100 thirteen-year-old boys spend the largest part of their pocket money on.

Complete the table to calculate the angle of each slice of a pie chart.

Activity or item	Number of boys	Angle of slice
Sports and hobbies	35	
Going out	15	
CDs, videos, DVDs	22	
Clothes	14	
Computer games	11	
Other	3	

1
(3 marks)

2 Draw a pie chart to show this information.

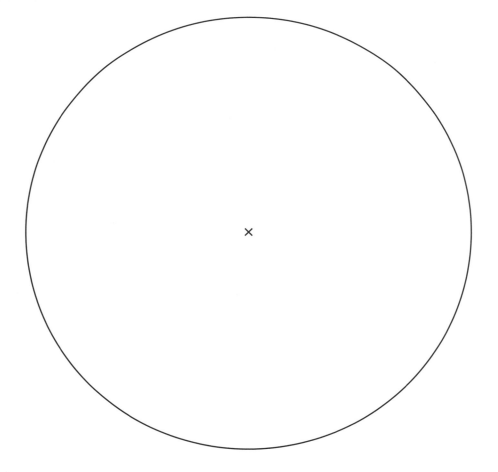

2
(3 marks)

/ 6

TOTAL MARKS

Probability – outcomes

Checking your understanding

1 Write down all the possible outcomes of rolling a dice and tossing a coin.

1

(1 mark)

2 In one bag there is a yellow ball, a blue ball and a green ball. In another bag there is a red ball and a pink ball. I take a ball from each bag. Draw a tree diagram to show all the possible outcomes.

2

(3 marks)

Using and applying

3 This spinner has equal sections with the numbers 1, 2 and 3.
Jo spins it twice and adds the numbers together to find a total.

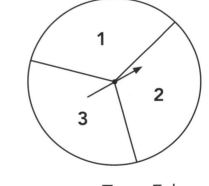

Tick to show whether each statement is true or false.

a) Jo is more likely to get the total 3 than 2.

True False
☐   ☐

b) Jo is as likely to get the total 3 as the total 5.

True False
☐   ☐

3

(3 marks)

c) Jo is less likely to get the total 6 than 2.

True False
☐   ☐

Explain in your own words how you worked out the answers to parts a, b and c.

/ 7

TOTAL MARKS

55

Mutually exclusive events

Checking your understanding

1 The probability of it snowing in December is $\frac{1}{11}$. What is the probability of it not snowing in December?

1
(1 mark)

2 The probability of rolling an even number 6 on a dice is $\frac{1}{2}$. What is the probability of not rolling an even number?

2
(1 mark)

3 In a pack of cards the probability that a card will be an ace is $\frac{1}{13}$. Find the probability it will not be an ace.

3
(1 mark)

4 P (a player will win a tennis match) = 0.7. What is the probability that the player will not win?

4
(1 mark)

Using and applying

5 All the pupils at Trinity School were asked in which season their birthdays fell. From the information gathered as part of this survey, the probabilities of a pupil having a birthday in each season are shown in this table.

Season	Spring	Summer	Autumn	Winter
Probability	0.2		0.3	0.15

a) Find the probability that a pupil has a summer birthday.

b) Find the probability that a pupil does NOT have a spring birthday.

5
(6 marks)

c) If there are 300 pupils at Trinity School, how many have an autumn birthday?

/ 10

TOTAL MARKS

Using and applying maths

1 Solve these problems.

a) Pete has £668. He buys as many computer games costing £59 each as he can with his money.

How much money does he have left?

b) In a shop, a coat costing £100 was incorrectly labelled £80. When the shopkeeper realised her mistake she increased the price to its original full price.

By what percentage did she increase the incorrect label price?

1

(2 marks)

2 A factory makes shapes from pieces of wire.

Write, as simply as possible, expressions to show the amount of wire needed to make each of these shapes, using the letters

a)

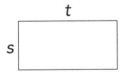

b)

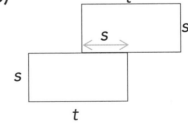

2

(8 marks)

c)

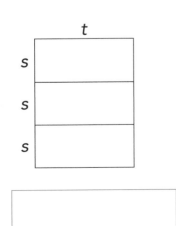

d)

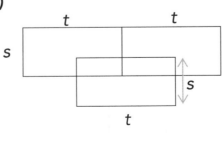

3 $2a + b = 16$ $a + b = 10$

Calculate the value of:

a) $3a$ [ ]   **b)** $2b$ [ ]   **c)** $5a + 3b$ [ ]

[ ] 3
(3 marks)

4 Fill in the missing numbers.

a) $\dfrac{\boxed{}}{60} = 0.6$ **b)** $\dfrac{35}{\boxed{}} = 70$

[ ] 4
(2 marks)

5 Solve these problems.

a) In a field are y cows and 4 people. There are 48 legs in the field. How many cows are there? [ ]

b) In a park are b dogs and 8 people. There are 52 legs in the park. How many dogs are there? [ ]

c) In a cellar there are t spiders and 5 people. There are 66 legs in the cellar. How many spiders are there? [ ]

[ ] 5
(3 marks)

6 In a room there are some people (x) and some fish (y).

There are 30 eyes and 20 legs. How many people are there and how many fish are there?

[ ]

[ ] 6
(2 marks)

7 Give the area of each shaded rectangle without using brackets.

a)

x + 4

2

b)

x + 2

x

c)

2x + 3

3

7

(3 marks)

8 Write a formula to match each of the cooking times in this recipe book. Call the number of minutes (*m*) and the number of kilograms of meat (*x*).

a) To quick-roast a chicken: Allow 30 minutes per kilogram and another 20 minutes extra.

b) To slow-roast lamb: Allow 35 minutes per $\frac{1}{2}$ kilogram and another 35 minutes extra.

8

(4 marks)

c) To quick-roast beef: Allow 20 minutes per $\frac{1}{2}$ kilogram and another 20 minutes extra.

d) To slow-roast a turkey: Allow 25 minutes per $\frac{1}{2}$ kilogram.

9 A jewelry shop makes brooches made from wire. Find the amount of wire used for this brooch to 1dp. Each diameter is 1.5 cm.

9

(2 marks)

10 How many sides has a regular polygon that has **exterior** angles of 20°?

10

(2 marks)

11 How many sides has a regular polygon that has **interior** angles of 150°?

11

(2 marks)

12 A smaller circle touches the circumference and centre of a larger circle as shown. The larger circle has a radius of 12 cm.

Find the area of the shaded region to the nearest whole number.

12

(3 marks)

/ 36

TOTAL MARKS